WeightWatchers®

D0358111

feasts from
the east

Azmina Govindji

SIMON & SCHUSTER
A VIACOM COMPANY

First published in Great Britain by Simon & Schuster, 1996
A Viacom Company

This edition produced for
The Book People Ltd
Hall Wood Avenue
Haydock
St Helens
WA11 9UL

First published 1996
Reprinted 2002

Simon & Schuster UK Ltd
Africa House
64–78 Kingsway
London WC2B 6AH

Design: Green Moore Lowenhoff
Cover design: Zoocity
Typesetting: Stylize
Photography: Karl Adamson
Styling: Maria Kelly
Food preparation: Jane Stevenson

ISBN 0-68481-801-9

Printed in Hong Kong

Recipe notes:
Egg size is medium, unless otherwise stated.
Vegetables are medium-sized, unless otherwise stated.
It is very important to use proper measuring spoons, not cutlery, for spoon measures.
1 tablespoon = 15 ml; 1 teaspoon = 5 ml
Dried herbs can be substituted for fresh ones, but the flavour may not always
be as good. Halve the fresh-herb quantity stated in the recipe.

Vegetarian recipes:
 shows the recipe is vegetarian.

Contents

Introduction

There was a time when following a diet meant eating only foods such as grilled fish and boiled vegetables. Fortunately, many diets now offer more variety and eye appeal. But did you ever imagine that Lemon Chicken or Bombay Potatoes could actually be part of a weight-loss Programme?

Weight Watchers *Feasts from the East* cookbook shows you how to experiment with classic Chinese, Indian and Thai dishes, using convenient ingredients readily available from supermarkets. There are no elaborate cooking methods or home-grinding of spices. Yet these quick-and-easy recipes will taste as exotic as those familiar restaurant favourites, while still helping you to keep to your diet.

The recipes are nutritionally balanced. Many of the Chinese dishes use vegetables which are lightly cooked, to preserve vitamins. Too much saturated fat can make you more prone to heart problems and the oils recommended in these recipes are low in saturated fat. So, these recipes are not only a welcome change to your regular diet, they're also a healthy way for the whole family to eat.

Cooking techniques

Use non-stick cookware so that you need the minimum amount of oil to prevent food from sticking. You don't necessarily need a wok for Chinese cooking; you can use an ordinary frying-pan instead.

Stir-frying is used widely in Chinese and Thai cooking. Small pieces of food are stirred around quickly, over intense heat, in a small amount of oil. If you have a wok, you'll find that the shape of the wok allows all the ingredients to get enough heat. The food is cooked in a matter of minutes and the vegetables retain their colour, texture and a lot of their nutrients.

Indian cooking requires no special utensils. In Indian cooking, onions and spices are generally shallow-fried in hot oil, before the main ingredients are added. These recipes need only small amounts of oil, and using ready-made spice pastes and powders means you spend less time cooking (and more time enjoying your meal!).

Special ingredients

While traditional Thai cooking includes ingredients such as special Thai ginger, lemon grass, fresh Thai basil leaves and fish sauce, these recipes take short-cuts by incorporating chopped ginger or crushed garlic from a jar, spring onions, lemon juice and dried basil. You can, of course, use fresh chopped ginger or crushed garlic if you prefer. Some recipes call for fish sauce, which contains anchovy extract. If you're not keen on this, simply omit it from the recipe or use soy sauce instead.

The Indian recipes use curry pastes and powders, which are sold in jars in supermarkets. Coriander is a must in Indian cooking and, although coriander paste is available, you may find it difficult to get hold of. You can use fresh coriander leaves, which are sold in 15 g (1/2 oz) packets in most supermarkets. If you don't need all of it for a recipe, store it in the fridge, wrapped in kitchen paper. This will absorb the moisture and help to keep it fresh for up to ten days. Coriander also freezes very well.

In general, cooking sauces and jars of pre-prepared ingredients are used, so there's no need to buy special "authentic" ingredients. A few essentials would be worth investing in, however, as these will allow you to try a whole range of recipes. Many can be kept in the fridge for future use. All of these are available from your supermarket and they are given below. You may choose to use a different brand of sauce from the one we recommend, but do remember that prepared sauces do contain Calories and Points so choose yours carefully, making sure to read the contents labels.

* Crushed, chopped or minced garlic (available in a jar)
* Crushed, chopped or minced ginger (available in a jar)
* Soy sauce (light soy sauce is thinner and saltier; dark soy sauce is thicker and sweeter)
* Curry paste (mild, medium or hot)
* Chilli powder
* Curry powder (mild, medium or hot)
* Chinese five-spice powder
* Fresh coriander leaves or coriander paste
* Dried basil
* Thai seven-spice powder
* Thai fish sauce

Rice

Gone are the days when rice was just plain boiled. Today you can complement your meal with many different types and here are just a few examples:

Egg-fried or special fried rice
This is a classic Chinese dish, in which rice is boiled and then fried with egg, meat or vegetables. The recipe in this book (page 34) uses only 1 teaspoon oil per person, to ensure it's low on Points but still high on taste.

Vegetable rice
This is a versatile dish that goes well with both Eastern and Western foods. It is usually made by boiling the rice first and then frying it in a little oil, with vegetables and spices.

Boiled rice
Easy to prepare: simply boil in lightly salted water, drain and serve. Ideally, choose basmati rice for your Indian meals and long-grain for Chinese or Thai dishes. However, it really doesn't matter too much and you can use whichever type you have available. Basmati rice takes 10–12 minutes to cook, whereas long-grain rice takes a little longer (12–15 minutes).

Thai Jasmine rice
A fragrant rice that has been scented with jasmine.

Pilau rice
A spicy Indian dish made with basmati rice and cumin, coriander and whole spices. The spices are fried with onions in a little oil and then meat or vegetables are added. The rice is cooked in the same pot, using just enough water for the rice to absorb . This ensures that none of the spice flavour is lost in drained water. As a short-cut, you could try the recipe for Indian Rice (page 32) and add your own spices and meat or vegetables. Delicious with a curry or simply with some low-fat natural yogurt.

Mushroom rice
This is a long-grain rice flavoured with mushrooms and (sometimes) other vegetables, and chicken stock. See page 35 if you want to cheat with this one and serve up a treat which takes only 10 minutes to prepare.

Accompaniments

It's all very well making meals that are low in Points and Calories but what about those accompaniments? Won't they ruin all that good work? Use the table below to help you choose healthy side dishes and fit them easily into your diet.

Serving size	Calories per serving	Points per serving
60 g (2 oz) boiled rice	200	1 $1/2$
60 g (2 oz) boiled egg noodles	220	1
1 pitta bread	165	2 $1/2$
1 mini pitta bread	80	1
1 fat-free chapati	130	1 $1/2$
$1/2$ piece naan bread	120	4
1 popadom, dry-grilled or microwaved	40	$1/2$
1 carton (150 ml) low-fat natural yogurt	40	1 $1/2$
2 teaspoons fat-free mango or tomato chutney	30	$1/2$

Remember to add Points for accompaniments not listed in the recipes. Points are given for main recipe only.

Meat and Fish Dishes

Tandoori chicken. . . sweet and sour pork. . . prawn biryani. . . those mouth-watering menus in restaurants may sound as though they're out of bounds on your weight-loss programme, but here's good news for you: all these dishes (and many more favourites) are here for you to try. And each one is made with quick and convenient ingredients. Experiment with the recipes in this chapter if you like tasty, exotic dishes that are low enough in Points to allow you a special meal on any day of a busy week.

Thai-spiced Chicken

Thai dishes tend to be quite spicy and often include vinegar or tamarind, which gives them that unique, sharp, fruity taste. The flavours of a Thai stir-fry cooking sauce are combined, in this recipe, with garlic and ginger, to make an aromatic meal in just 20 minutes.

Serves: 2
Preparation and cooking time: 20 minutes
Calories per serving: 460
Points per serving: 9
Total Points per recipe: 18
Freezing: recommended

90 g (3 oz) long-grain rice
3 teaspoons corn or rapeseed oil

8 cm (3-inch) piece of fresh leek, sliced
4 spring onions, cut in 1 cm (¹/₂-inch) pieces
1 teaspoon crushed garlic
1 teaspoon crushed ginger
240 g (8 oz) boneless, skinless chicken breast,
    sliced thinly
200 g jar of Thai stir-fry basil and chilli sauce
225 g can of water chestnuts, halved or sliced
salt

❶ Cook the rice in plenty of lightly salted, boiling water for about 12 minutes, until just tender. Drain.

❷ Meanwhile, heat a wok or non-stick pan. Swirl in 2 teaspoons of oil and add the leek and most of the spring onions. Save the remaining spring onions for garnish. Stir-fry over a high heat for a couple of minutes. Remove from the pan.

❸ Pour the extra teaspoon of oil into the pan. Add the garlic, ginger and chicken. Stir-fry till the chicken pieces are browned.

❹ Return the cooked onions and leek to the pan. Pour in the basil and chilli sauce and add the water chestnuts. Stir well and add 2 tablespoons of hot water. Continue cooking until the sauce is heated through.

❺ Sprinkle on the remaining spring onions and serve with the boiled rice.

Vegetarian option: Substitute 240 g (8 oz) of frozen Chinese vegetables for the chicken and deduct 2¹/₂ Points or 175 Calories per serving.

Variation:
Instead of the chicken, use 480 g (1 lb) of firm white fish or peeled, cooked prawns. This will add 1 Point or 95 Calories per serving.

Coriander Chicken Curry

This dish is a blend of a Thai 'green curry' and an Indian chicken curry. The recipe recommends you use boneless chicken but you can use chicken on the bone, if you prefer. The Thai version would include coconut milk, which is high in Points, so low-fat natural yogurt is recommended instead. Serve with rice, chapatis or naan bread.

Serves: 2
Preparation time: 10 minutes
Cooking time: 10 minutes
Calories per serving: 220
Points per serving: 4
Total Points per recipe: 8
Freezing: recommended

2 teaspoons rapeseed or corn oil
1 onion, sliced finely

1 teaspoon crushed garlic
1 teaspoon crushed ginger
240 g (8 oz) boneless, skinless chicken breast,
    cut in small pieces
1 teaspoon curry powder
1/2 teaspoon chilli powder, or to taste
2 tablespoons low-fat natural yogurt
2 x 15 g packets of fresh coriander, chopped
salt and coarsely ground black pepper

❶ Heat a pan. Add the oil and stir-fry the onion, garlic and ginger for a few minutes.
❷ Add the chicken, curry powder, chilli powder and seasoning. Stir-fry until the chicken is cooked (around 10 minutes).
❸ Stir in the yogurt, coriander and a tablespoon of hot water. Heat through over a medium heat for 4–5 minutes.

Vegetarian option: Substitute 240 g (8 oz) of peeled, cubed potatoes and 120 g (4 oz) of peas for the chicken. Add the peas at step 3. Freezing is not recommended for this version, which reduces the Calories to 205 and the Points per serving to 3.

Tandoori Chicken

A classic Indian dish that needs only a crisp salad as an accompaniment. If you would prefer to have a more filling dish, this goes well with naan or pitta bread and some low-fat natural yogurt.

Serves: 1
Preparation time: 5 minutes + 10 minutes
    marinating
Cooking time: 20 minutes
Calories per serving: 190
Total Points per recipe: 3 1/2
Freezing: recommended

90 g (3 oz) boneless, skinless chicken breast
1 teaspoon rapeseed or olive oil
1 1/2 teaspoons tandoori spice mix
2 tablespoons low-fat natural yogurt
1/2 teaspoon curry powder
salt
juice of 1/2 a lemon

❶ Preheat the grill. Pierce the chicken breast with a skewer or fork, to allow the marinade to penetrate Make diagonal cuts on both sides of the chicken.
❷ Mix all the other ingredients together. Coat the chicken on both sides with this marinade and refrigerate for 10 minutes.

❸ Line a flameproof dish with cooking foil. Grill the chicken under a high heat for 10 minutes on each side. Serve hot or cold.

Coriander Chicken Curry
Tandoori Chicken

Lemon Chicken

This sweet and sour dish requires virtually no cooking skills! Serve with boiled rice.

Serves: 2
Preparation time: 10 minutes
Cooking time: 20 minutes
Calories per serving: 420
Points per serving: 7$^1/_2$
Total Points per recipe: 15
Freezing: not recommended

90 g (3 oz) long-grain rice
1 teaspoon cornflour
1 tablespoon soy sauce
3 drops of sesame oil
2 × 120 g (4 oz) boneless,
    skinless chicken breasts
2 teaspoons rapeseed or corn oil
120 g sachet of Peking lemon sauce
salt and pepper

❶ Cook the rice in plenty of boiling, lightly salted water for about 12 minutes, until just tender.

❷ Meanwhile, sprinkle the cornflour, salt, pepper, soy sauce and sesame oil over the chicken.

❸ Heat the rapeseed oil in a wok or non-stick frying-pan with a lid. Fry the chicken breasts over a high heat, until browned on both sides.

❹ Lower the heat and add a tablespoon of hot water. Cover and simmer for 15–20 minutes, or until the chicken is cooked.

❺ Coat the chicken with the lemon sauce and heat through.

Variation: Substitute 2 × 210 g (7 oz) fish fillets for the chicken. This increases the Points to 8$^1/_2$ and decreases the Calories to 365 per serving.

Cook's notes: The sauce is quite thick. If you prefer a more runny sauce, add an extra 2–3 tablespoons of hot water when cooking the chicken.

You may find it more economical to buy boneless chicken with the skin and remove the skin yourself.

If you have time, flatten the chicken with a mallet or rolling pin before frying. It will absorb the lemon flavour better.

Sweet and Sour Pork

Sweet and sour dishes often involve coating the pork or chicken in batter and then deep-frying it. In this recipe, the pork is coated in seasoned cornflour and then stir-fried in just a little oil. Leeks combine well with pork and here they are separated into rings and stir-fried with the pork.

Serves: 4
Preparation time: 15 minutes
Cooking time: 5 minutes
Calories per serving: 360
Points per serving: 6
Total Points per recipe: 24
Freezing: recommended

300 g (10 oz) lean pork, cut in small cubes
240 g (8 oz) long-grain rice
1 tablespoon sesame or corn oil
1 leek, sliced thinly and separated into rings
120 g sachet of sweet and sour sauce
For the marinade:
¹/₂ teaspoon salt
1 tablespoon light soy sauce
1 teaspoon cornflour

❶ Mix the marinade ingredients together and coat the pork with this marinade. Set aside while you cook the rice.

❷ Cook the rice in lightly salted water for 12–15 minutes. Drain and keep warm.

❸ Heat a wok or large, non-stick frying-pan with a lid. Swirl in a teaspoon of the oil and stir-fry the leeks for about a minute. Remove from the pan.

❹ Heat the remaining oil and stir-fry the pork for 3–4 minutes.

❺ Stir in the sweet and sour sauce and a tablespoon of hot water. Add the leeks, cover and simmer for

about 5 minutes, until the pork is cooked. Serve immediately, with the rice.

Vegetarian option: Substitute a 285 g packet of beancurd (tofu) for the pork and deduct 1 Point and 35 Calories per serving.

Variation: Use 360 g (12 oz) of boneless, skinless chicken, instead of the pork. This will add 15 Calories. The Points will be reduced by 1 Point per serving.

Pork and Pepper Stir-fry

Stir-fries are always a great supper idea on those days you just don't have time (or desire!) to spend ages in the kitchen.

Serves: 4

Preparation time and cooking time: 20 minutes + marinating

Calories per serving: 160

Points per serving: 3

Total Points per recipe: 12

Freezing: recommended

300 g (10 oz) lean pork, cut in small cubes
1 tablespoon rapeseed or corn oil
1 green pepper, de-seeded and chopped roughly
1 yellow pepper, de-seeded and chopped roughly

1 large onion, chopped finely
1/2 teaspoon Chinese five-spice powder
1/4 teaspoon sugar

For the marinade:
1/3 teaspoon salt
1 tablespoon light soy sauce
2 teaspoons medium-dry sherry
1 teaspoon cornflour
1 tablespoon oyster sauce
1/2 teaspoon crushed ginger
pepper

❶ Mix the marinade ingredients together and coat the pork with the marinade. Refrigerate for up to an hour.

❷ Heat a wok or non-stick frying-pan. Swirl in a teaspoon of the oil and stir-fry the peppers and onion for a couple of minutes. Remove and set aside.

❸ Heat the remaining oil. Add the marinated pork and stir-fry until browned.

❹ Add the five-spice powder, sugar, peppers and onion. Stir-fry until all the ingredients are just cooked. Serve with boiled rice or noodles.

Vegetarian option: Substitute a 285 g packet of beancurd (tofu) for the pork and deduct 1 Point and 35 Calories per serving.

Weight Watchers note: Remember to add the Points for the rice or noodles.

Variations: Use 360 g (12 oz) of boneless, skinless chicken breast, cubed, instead of the pork. Add 15 Calories per serving but deduct 1 Point.

Or use 360 g (12 oz) lean beef, cubed. Again add 15 Calories per serving, but this time the Points remain the same as for the main recipe.

Fish Korma

A korma is usually very rich and can be made with almonds and cream. This is a lighter version which is (unconventionally) cooked in the oven, so you can spend less time watching it.

Serves: 4
Preparation time: 20 minutes
Cooking time: 20 minutes
Calories per serving: 165
Points per serving: 3
Total Points per recipe: 12
Freezing: recommended

2 teaspoons olive or corn oil
1 onion, chopped finely

1 teaspoon crushed garlic
1 teaspoon crushed ginger
300 g jar of Weight Watchers from Heinz korma cooking sauce
1 teaspoon Madras curry paste (optional)
15 g packet of fresh coriander leaves, chopped roughly
4 frozen haddock fillets
1 teaspoon dried basil
salt and freshly ground black pepper

❶ Preheat the oven to Gas Mark 5/190°C/375°F. Heat a pan. Swirl in the oil and add the onion, garlic and ginger. Stir-fry for 5 minutes over a moderate heat.
❷ Add the cooking sauce, curry paste, if using, and coriander. Mix well and remove from the heat.
❸ Lightly grease a flat ovenproof dish. Arrange the fish at the bottom of the dish and sprinkle with salt, pepper and basil.
❹ Pour the sauce over the fish and coat well. Cook in the oven for 20–25 minutes and serve hot, with plain boiled rice.

Cook's notes: Fresh coriander is ideal for this recipe, because it gives a crunchy texture.

You can defrost the fish before cooking if you prefer, although the packaging on bought frozen fish usually specifies that it should be cooked from frozen.

Weight Watchers note: Remember to add the Points for the rice.

Variation: Instead of fish, you can use 240 g (8 oz) of boneless, skinless chicken breast or turkey breast, which will reduce the Calories to 140 per serving, and the Points to 2¹/₂; or use 210 g (7 oz) of lean pork, which will reduce the Calories to 135 per serving. The Points will stay the same.

Prawn Biryani

A special-occasion meal that goes well with natural yogurt and Coriander and Coconut Chutney (page 42).

Serves: 2
Preparation and cooking time: 30 minutes
Calories per serving: 240
Points per serving: $4^1/_2$
Total Points per recipe: 9
Freezing: not recommended

60 g (2 oz) basmati rice
2 teaspoons olive or corn oil
1 teaspoon crushed garlic
1 teaspoon crushed ginger
1 small onion, chopped finely

60 g (2 oz) cooked, peeled prawns,
    defrosted if frozen
2 tablespoons canned chopped tomatoes
1 teaspoon curry powder
$^1/_4$ teaspoon chilli powder
2 tablespoons low-fat natural yogurt
1 teaspoon coriander paste or 1 tablespoon
    chopped fresh coriander
1 tablespoon sultanas
1 tablespoon flaked or chopped almonds
salt

1 Boil the rice in plenty of lightly salted, boiling water and drain.

2 Heat a pan. Add the oil and then the garlic, ginger and onion. Stir-fry until the onion turns brown.

3 Add the prawns and stir for a minute or so. Add the tomatoes, curry powder, salt, chilli powder, yogurt, coriander and a tablespoon of hot water. Cook this over a low heat, stirring frequently. The mixture should be quite thick.

4 Add the cooked rice and stir very gently. Cover and leave over a low heat until the rice is heated through.

5 Serve on warmed plates and top with the sultanas and almonds.

Vegetarian option: Use 120 g (4 oz) of canned red kidney beans, instead of the prawns. Add 35 Calories per serving and $^1/_2$ Point per serving.

Cook's note: You may prefer to serve the rice as a base and top this with the prawn mixture, rather than mixing the rice and prawns before serving.

Variation: Use 60 g (2 oz) of cubed boneless, skinless turkey or chicken breast, instead of the prawns. Add 10 Calories per serving. The Points remain the same.

Balti Beef Curry

Indian Balti meals originate from Northern India and Pakistan. A 'Balti' dish is similar to a wok and you may be served a restaurant Balti meal in an individual-size Balti dish.

Serves: 4
Preparation time: 15 minutes
Cooking time: 45 minutes
Calories per serving: 355
Points per serving: 6$\frac{1}{2}$
Total Points per recipe: 26
Freezing: recommended

240 g (8 oz) basmati rice
240 g (8 oz) lean beef, cubed
1 teaspoon crushed garlic
1 teaspoon crushed ginger
283 g jar of Balti cooking sauce
15 g packet of fresh coriander leaves, chopped
2 fresh tomatoes, halved
150 ml carton of low-fat natural yogurt
salt

1 Boil the rice in plenty of lightly salted, boiling water, for about 10 minutes; drain.

2 Heat a non-stick pan or wok with a lid. Brown the beef over a high heat for about 5 minutes.

3 Add the garlic, ginger and a good pinch of salt and stir well.

4 Stir in the cooking sauce, coriander and 3 tablespoons of hot water. Cover and simmer until the beef is cooked, adding more water as required.

5 Lower the tomato halves into the pan. Cover and allow the tomatoes to heat through and become slightly softened. Serve with the boiled rice and natural yogurt.

Vegetarian option: Replace the beef with 150 g (5 oz) of cubed potato and 120 g (4 oz) of chick-peas. Deduct 10 Calories and 1 Point per serving.

Variation: Use the same weight of boneless, skinless chicken or turkey breast, cubed, or 210 g (7 oz) of lean pork. Deduct 10 Calories and 1 Point per serving.

Stir-fried Beef in Szechuan Sauce

Szechuan cooking originates from a province in western China. This recipe makes use of a Weight Watchers cooking sauce, so there's no need for you to worry about buying any special ingredients. The sauce has just the right amount of spiciness, which is counteracted by a slightly sweet taste. Serve with plain boiled rice.

Serves: 4
Preparation time: 20 minutes
Cooking time: 20 minutes
Calories per serving: 170
Points per serving: 3
Total Points per recipe: 12
Freezing: recommended

1 teaspoon rapeseed or corn oil
1 onion, chopped finely
1/2 teaspoon crushed garlic
300 g (10 oz) lean beef, cut in thin strips
295 g jar of Weight Watchers from Heinz
    Szechuan cooking sauce
2 tablespoons soy sauce
300 g (10 oz) frozen broccoli florets

❶ Heat a wok or non-stick pan with a lid. Swirl in the oil. Add the onion and garlic and stir-fry for about 3 minutes.

❷ Add the beef. Stir-fry over a high heat for 5 minutes.

❸ Add the cooking sauce, soy sauce and 180 ml (6 fl oz) of hot water. Stir well. Cover and cook over a moderate heat for 15 minutes.

❹ Add the broccoli and another 150 ml (1/4 pint) of hot water. Cover and cook till the broccoli is just cooked and the meat is tender (about 5 minutes). Serve with plain boiled rice.

Vegetarian option: Use 500 g (1 lb) of frozen Chinese vegetables, instead of the beef, and deduct 2 Points and 40 Calories per serving.

Cook's note: Add more water, if you prefer a more runny sauce.

Weight Watchers note: Remember to include Points for the rice.

Variation: Use 300 g (10 oz) of chicken breast, or 240 g (8 oz) of lean pork, instead of the beef. Substitute 250 g (8 oz) of mange-tout for the broccoli. This will reduce the Points per serving to 2 1/2 if using chicken and 3 Points if using pork.

Lamb Tikka

This spicy dish reminds me of the lamb kebabs that are sold on the streets of India and Pakistan. It is traditionally cooked on a charcoal grill and served with lemon wedges and raw onion rings. In this recipe, the tiny cubes of lamb are skewered with chunks of onion and served with a crisp salad and warmed pitta bread.

Serves: 4
Preparation time: 20 minutes + marinating
Cooking time: 20 minutes
Calories per serving: 140
Points per serving: 4
Total Points per recipe: 16
Freezing: not recommended

240 g (8 oz) lean lamb, cut in small cubes
1 onion, quartered and separated into layers
For the marinade:
2 teaspoons rapeseed or corn oil

2 teaspoons lemon juice
1 teaspoon crushed garlic
1 teaspoon crushed ginger
150 ml (1/4 pint) low-fat natural yogurt
1 teaspoon curry powder
1 tablespoon rogan josh curry paste
1/4 teaspoon salt
To serve:
4 mini pitta breads, warmed
mixed, undressed salad
lemon juice or lemon wedges

❶ Mix the marinade ingredients together. Coat the lamb pieces with this sauce and leave to marinate for at least an hour.

❷ Preheat the grill. Line the grill-pan with cooking foil. Thread the lamb and onion layers alternately on to bamboo or metal skewers. Pour any leftover marinade on to the skewers.

❸ Grill under a medium heat for about 20 minutes, turning regularly. Serve hot, with warmed pitta bread, mixed salad and lemon juice or wedges of lemon.

Vegetarian option: Substitute 450 g (15 oz) of beancurd (tofu) for the lamb. Deduct 1 Point and 15 Calories per serving.

Cook's notes: If you prefer a hotter marinade, use vindaloo curry paste instead.

If you use wooden or bamboo skewers, soak them in water for an hour first, to stop them from burning during cooking.

Variations: Instead of the lamb, use 330 g (11 oz) of chicken or turkey and add 25 Calories per serving and subtract 1/2 Point. Or use 270 g (9 oz) lean pork and add 10 Calories per serving, or 480 g (1 lb) of firm white fish, and add 20 Calories per serving. The Points will remain the same for the pork and fish.

Vegetable Dishes

This chapter has a nutritious array of colourful vegetarian choices, ranging from simple stir-fried vegetables to spicy Bombay Potatoes (page 28). Most of the vegetables are cooked only lightly, to preserve their vitamins and also to retain a firm, crunchy texture. Many are so low in Points that you can fill yourself up on large portions, or have some extra side-dishes and still keep to your diet. And for those of you who like your veggies mixed with a bit of meat, simply refer to the 'Meat Options' at the end of some recipes.

Mushrooms in Oyster Sauce, with Noodles

The crunchy onions in this stir-fry contrast beautifully with the soft noodles. A massive portion, for days when your eyes are bigger than your stomach!

Serves: 1
Preparation and cooking time: 25 minutes
Calories per serving: 455
Total Points per recipe: 6¹/₂
Freezing: recommended

Ⓥ if using a vegetable stock cube

60 g (2 oz) thread egg noodles
3 teaspoons corn or rapeseed oil

1 small onion, sliced
¹/₄ teaspoon crushed ginger
240 g (8 oz) mushrooms, sliced
For the oyster sauce:
2 tablespoons oyster sauce
¹/₂ chicken or vegetable stock cube, dissolved in
    5 tablespoons boiling water
1 tablespoon soy sauce
salt and freshly ground black pepper
a few fresh coriander or parsley sprigs, chopped

❶ Cook the noodles in slightly salted, boiling water, according to the instructions on the packet. Drain and keep warm.
❷ Heat a wok or non-stick frying-pan. Add 2 teaspoons of oil, the onion and ginger. Stir-fry for 3 minutes.
❸ Pour in the remaining teaspoon of oil and add the mushrooms. Stir-fry for a couple of minutes.
❹ Mix the ingredients for the oyster sauce and add this to the mushrooms. Blend well and heat through.

❺ Sprinkle in the fresh coriander and serve in a ring of noodles.

Cook's note: For extra flavour, add ¹/₂ teaspoon Chinese five-spice powder to the oyster sauce mixture.

Meat option: Substitute 60 g (2 oz) of lean beef for the mushrooms and add 2 Points and 40 Calories per serving.

Mushroom in Oyster Sauce, with Noodles

Sweet and Sour Beancurd

Beancurd is also known by the Japanese name 'tofu'. It is rich in protein, low in Calories and Points and has an interesting spongy texture. It is usually deep-fried but, in this recipe, the beancurd is brushed with oil and grilled, to give it the characteristic crisp surface without piling on the Points.

Serves: 4
Preparation and cooking time: 45 minutes
Calories per serving: 215
Points per serving: 3
Total Points per recipe: 12
Freezing: not recommended

285 g packet of beancurd (tofu), cut in small cubes
1 tablespoon light soy sauce
2 tablespoons corn oil
2 teaspoons sesame oil
1 teaspoon crushed garlic
1 teaspoon crushed ginger

1 onion, sliced
1 green pepper, de-seeded and cut in fine strips
300 g (10 oz) button mushrooms
210 g (7 oz) canned pineapple pieces in natural juice, drained
a few fresh coriander sprigs, chopped finely
For the sauce:
1¹/₂ tablespoons tomato purée
3 spring onions, sliced finely
1 tablespoon cider vinegar
1 tablespoon dry sherry
1 tablespoon light soy sauce
2 teaspoons honey
2 teaspoons cornflour, mixed with 2 tablespoons water
salt, to taste

1 Toss the beancurd cubes in soy sauce and leave to marinate for 5 minutes. Meanwhile, preheat the grill and line the grill pan with foil.

2 Brush the beancurd with some of the corn oil and grill under a moderate heat for 15–20 minutes, until the cubes are golden brown. Turn once during cooking.

3 Heat the remaining corn oil and the sesame oil in a wok or non-stick frying-pan. Add the garlic and ginger and sauté for a few seconds.

4 Add the onion and pepper and stir-fry over a high heat until softened (about 5 minutes). Now add the mushrooms and stir-fry till they are just cooked.

5 Combine all the sauce ingredients, *except* the cornflour paste in a small pan with 300 ml (¹/₂ pint)

of water. Bring to the boil. Lower the heat and add the cornflour paste. Bring slowly to the boil again, stirring to prevent any lumps from forming.

6 Pour the sauce over the vegetables in the wok and stir well. Slowly stir in the grilled beancurd and drained pineapple pieces. Heat through, add the chopped coriander and serve.

Weight Watchers note: This is a home-made sweet and sour sauce. If you want to use a short-cut, try using a 300 g jar of Weight Watchers from Heinz Sweet and Sour Sauce instead.

Stir-fried Courgettes and Red Peppers

This brightly coloured dish, made with crunchy vegetables, looks too good to eat! The veggies are cooked quickly over a high heat to preserve the vitamins. It's so low in Points that you may want to serve it as a side dish or with a more special type of rice, such as Egg-fried Rice (see page 34).

Serves: 2
Preparation and cooking time: 20 minutes
Calories per serving: 225
Points per serving: 2¹/₂
Total Points per recipe: 5
Freezing: not recommended

60 g (2 oz) long-grain rice
2 teaspoons rapeseed or corn oil
4 spring onions, sliced diagonally in 1 cm
 (¹/₂-inch) strips
1 red pepper, de-seeded and chopped
1 teaspoon crushed garlic
3 courgettes, sliced thinly
2 tablespoons light soy sauce
1 teaspoon Chinese five-spice powder
a few drops of chilli sauce (optional)
salt and freshly ground black pepper

❶ Cook the rice in plenty of lightly salted, boiling water for about 12 minutes, until just tender. Drain.
❷ Heat a wok or large non-stick frying-pan. Swirl in the oil. Add the spring onions and pepper and stir-fry for 3 minutes.
❸ Add all the other ingredients and stir-fry until cooked but still crunchy, about 8–10 minutes. Serve with the rice.

Fish or meat option: Add 60 g (2 oz) of defrosted peeled, cooked prawns or drained, flaked tuna fish in brine, or 30 g (1 oz) of chopped, cooked ham. This will provide 1 extra Point and 30 Calories per serving.

Variation: You could use a variety of fresh, frozen or canned vegetables instead of the courgettes and peppers.

Creamy Curried Lentils

This is a highly popular and nutritious dish and is eaten almost daily in India. It is delicious with plain boiled basmati rice and low-fat natural yogurt. When I'm in a hurry, I often serve it in a pitta pocket, with shredded lettuce.

Serves: 2
Preparation time: 10 minutes
Cooking time: 15 minutes
Calories per serving: 180
Points per serving: 2¹/₂
Total Points per recipe: 5
Freezing: recommended

2 teaspoons olive or rapeseed oil
1 small onion, chopped finely
¹/₂ teaspoon crushed garlic
¹/₂ teaspoon crushed ginger
1 teaspoon rogan josh curry paste
4 tablespoons canned chopped tomatoes
¹/₄ teaspoon chilli powder or 1 fresh green chilli, de-seeded and chopped finely
60 g (2 oz) split red lentils
¹/₄ teaspoon salt
a few drops of lemon juice
a few finely chopped sprigs of fresh coriander

❶ Heat the oil. Fry the onion for a few minutes until softened, stirring frequently to prevent it from burning. Add the garlic and ginger and stir well.

❷ Add the curry paste, tomatoes and chilli powder or chilli. Cook for 5 minutes over a moderate heat, until creamy.

❸ Add the lentils and 120 ml (4 fl oz) of hot water. Cover and simmer for 10 minutes, until the lentils are cooked but not mushy. If the lentils are not cooked after 10 minutes, add a little more hot water and cook until the water is absorbed.

❹ Gently stir in the salt, lemon juice and coriander.

Cook's note: If you prefer more sauce, add a few tablespoons of hot water and stir gently.

Weight Watchers note: Remember to add the Points for the accompaniments.

Variation: You could substitute any dried lentils or beans for the red lentils but, if you do, refer to cooking instructions on the packaging, as cooking times may vary.

Bombay Potatoes

This quick-and-easy dish is an excellent way to spice up leftover potatoes.

Serves: 2
Preparation and cooking time: 20 minutes
Calories per serving: 150
Points per serving: 3
Total Points per recipe: 6
Freezing: not recommended

300 g (10 oz) new potatoes, scrubbed or peeled
    and cut in small cubes

1 teaspoon corn oil
¹/₂ teaspoon mustard seeds
¹/₂ teaspoon crushed garlic
1 heaped tablespoon canned chopped tomatoes
2 teaspoons rogan josh curry paste
15 g packet of fresh coriander leaves, chopped
    finely
salt and freshly ground black pepper
To serve:
2 mini pitta breads
shredded lettuce

❶ Boil the potatoes until just tender.
❷ Heat the oil in a non-stick saucepan. Remove from the heat, add the mustard seeds and cover with a lid. You should hear the mustard seeds popping.
❸ Uncover when the popping sounds get slower and return the pan to the heat. Add the garlic, salt, pepper, tomatoes and curry paste. Stir-fry for a few minutes.
❹ Add the cooked potatoes, 105 ml (3¹/₂ fl oz) of hot water and coriander. Cover and simmer until the potatoes absorb the spices (about 5 minutes). Serve in, or with, warmed mini pittas and shredded lettuce.

Spinach and Potato Curry

If ever you feel like cheating by using cans and pastes, but still want to be able to rustle up a genuine Indian meal, this is the dish to choose. I suggest you keep these canned vegetables in your larder for days when you've run out of cooking ideas.

Serves: 3
Preparation time: 15 minutes
Cooking time: 5 minutes
Calories per serving: 150
Points per serving: 2
Total Points per recipe: 6
Freezing: not recommended

1 tablespoon rapeseed or corn oil

1 onion, chopped
2 bay leaves (optional)
1 teaspoon crushed garlic
2 fresh tomatoes, chopped finely, or 2 tablespoons
    canned chopped tomatoes
2 fresh green chillies, de-seeded and chopped
    finely, or ¹/₄–¹/₂ teaspoon chilli powder
2 teaspoons rogan josh curry paste
300 g can of new potatoes, drained
270 g can of spinach leaf, drained
salt

❶ Heat a wok or non-stick frying-pan with a lid and swirl in the oil. Add the onion, bay leaves, if using, and garlic. Fry for 3 minutes, until the onion is browned.
❷ Stir in the tomatoes, chillies or chilli powder, curry paste and salt. Stir-fry for 2–3 minutes.
❸ Add the potatoes and spinach and mix well.
❹ Stir in 2 tablespoons of hot water, cover and simmer for 5 minutes.

Spinach and Potato Curry
Bombay Potatoes

Vegetable Kebabs with Peanut Sauce

This is a variation of a Thai recipe that would normally be made with fresh basil leaves, fresh chillies and lime. This dish is made with dried basil, chilli powder and lemon juice. There's no cooking involved in the peanut sauce, which takes less than 5 minutes to prepare.

Serves: 1
Preparation and cooking time: 35–40 minutes
Calories per serving: 390
Total Points per recipe: 5¹/₂
Freezing: not recommended

1 courgette, cut in 1 cm (¹/₂-inch) slices
1 onion, quartered and separated into layers
90 g (3 oz) button mushrooms
1 red pepper, de-seeded and cut in 2.5 cm
    (1-inch) squares
90 g (3 oz) canned pineapple chunks in natural
    juice, drained

For the marinade:
2 teaspoons olive oil
1 tablespoon light soy sauce
1 teaspoon dried basil
¹/₄ teaspoon chilli powder
¹/₂ teaspoon Thai seven-spice or
        Chinese five-spice powder
¹/₄ teaspoon crushed garlic (optional)
¹/₄ teaspoon crushed ginger
a pinch of salt
For the peanut sauce:
1 tablespoon sugar-free crunchy peanut butter
1 teaspoon lemon juice
2 teaspoons desiccated coconut
¹/₄ teaspoon chilli powder

❶ Thread the vegetables and pineapple on to skewers. Mix the marinade ingredients together and pour this sauce over the kebabs. Set aside while you prepare the peanut sauce.
❷ Preheat the grill. Prepare the peanut sauce by mixing all the ingredients together with 3 tablespoons of water.
❸ Put the kebabs in a shallow, flameproof dish. Pour any remaining marinade over the kebabs and grill until cooked. Turn and baste frequently during this time. Serve immediately, with the peanut sauce.

Cook's notes: Thai seven-spice powder is a wonderfully spicy mixture available from most supermarkets and all oriental foodshops.

The kebabs should look slightly charred and are cooked until the courgettes are tender but still firm.

If you prefer a browned peanut sauce, you can heat it in a microwave or a small non-stick pan for a few seconds.

Meat option: Thread 90 g (3 oz) of boneless, skinless chicken on to the skewers, with the onion and pineapple only. This will add 2 Points and 20 Calories per serving.

Variations: You can use tomatoes, cucumber, shallots and beancurd (tofu) instead of some of these vegetables.

If you are making this dish for more than one person, choose red and yellow peppers to give more colour. Otherwise, just double up the ingredient quantities for two people.

Speedy Vegetable Chow-mein

This substantial dish needs no accompaniments. Although chow-mein is actually a Chinese dish, this recipe is more of a Thai version, especially if you use the seven-spice powder. This recipe is wonderfully spicy and makes use of a packet of instant noodles, which simply need to be soaked for a few minutes while you stir-fry the vegetables. The noodles do come with a sachet of chow-mein mix, which you can use if you like. I prefer to use the ingredients in this recipe.

Serves: 3
Preparation and cooking time: 15 minutes
Calories per serving: 235
Points per serving: 2¹/₂
Total Points per recipe: 7¹/₂
Freezing: not recommended

85 g packet of instant chow-mein noodles
1 tablespoon corn oil
4 spring onions, cut diagonally in 1 cm (¹/₂-inch)
  slices

1 teaspoon crushed garlic
1 teaspoon crushed ginger
2 carrots, cut in thin strips or diagonal slices
90 g (3 oz) frozen peas
1 teaspoon Madras curry paste
¹/₄ teaspoon Thai seven-spice powder or Chinese
  five-spice powder
¹/₂ teaspoon dried basil
a pinch of sugar
2 tablespoons light soy sauce
120 g (4 oz) button mushrooms
salt

1 Soak the noodles in hot, lightly salted water according to the instructions on the packet. Drain and rinse in cold running water.

2 Heat a wok or non-stick frying-pan and swirl in the oil. Add all the other ingredients in the order they appear in the ingredients list. Stir well after each addition.

3 Continue to stir-fry for a few minutes over a high heat until the vegetables are cooked. Season with a pinch of salt.

4 Gently stir in the noodles, adjust the seasoning, if necessary, and serve as soon as the noodles are heated through.

Cook's note: Thai seven-spice powder is available from most supermarkets – you'll find it in the dried herbs section.

Side Dishes and Starters

I
dian, Chinese and Thai cooking is all about combining a variety of colourful and often spicy dishes, which are eaten together to form a main meal. Use this section to help you choose appropriate accompaniments to your Eastern-style meal. All of the Indian dishes go well with Indian Rice (below) and there are Chinese noodle and rice dishes for you to choose from, too. Add a bit of tang to your menu by making a chutney (relax, it only takes 5 minutes!) or a refreshing raita. You may also like to choose items from this chapter for your main meal. For example, Mushroom Rice (page 35) with Diced Spiced Salad (page 36) is an unusual meal which takes only half an hour from the start of preparation to putting food on the table.

Indian Rice

The basmati rice in this recipe is cooked in steam in a tightly closed saucepan. All of the water is absorbed and the aromatic spices provide a very 'Indian' touch to any main dish. If you don't have these particular spices, substitute a few cloves, three or four whole black peppercorns and a good pinch of grated nutmeg.

Serves: 2
Preparation time: 5 minutes + 15 minutes soaking
Cooking time: 10 minutes
Calories per serving: 100
Points per serving: 1$^{1}/_{2}$
Total Points per recipe: 3
Freezing: recommended

60 g (2 oz) basmati rice, rinsed
5 cm (2-inch) cinnamon stick, broken
$^{1}/_{2}$ teaspoon cumin seeds
$^{1}/_{4}$ teaspoon salt

(V)

1 Soak the rice in plenty of warm water for about 15 minutes.
2 Put the drained rice, all the other ingredients and 150 ml ($^{1}/_{4}$ pint) of boiling water into a saucepan with a tightly fitting lid. Cover and simmer over a very low heat for 10 minutes, until all the water is absorbed.

3 Uncover, stir gently and serve hot.

Cook's notes: If you add a slice of lemon to the pan with the other ingredients, this will prevent the rice from sticking together.
  To extend this recipe for four people, simply double all the ingredients, including the water.

Egg-fried Rice

Is this possible? 'Egg-fried rice' on a weight-loss Programme? This recipe uses the minimum amount of oil yet still gives you that familiar Chinese appearance and flavour.

Serves: 2
Preparation and cooking time: 15 minutes
Calories per serving: 190
Points per serving: 3½
Total Points per recipe: 7
Freezing: not recommended

60 g (2 oz) long-grain rice
2 teaspoons sesame or corn oil
1 egg, beaten
3 spring onions, sliced
1 teaspoon crushed ginger (optional)
2 teaspoons soy sauce

❶ Rinse the rice in cold water and cook in plenty of lightly salted, boiling water for 10–12 minutes. Drain and rinse under cold running water, to separate the grains.

❷ While the rice is cooking, heat a teaspoon of the oil in a wok or non-stick frying-pan. Pour in the beaten egg and allow it to set in the base of the pan. Scramble the egg and remove it from the pan.

❸ Heat the remaining teaspoon of oil. Add the spring onions and ginger (if used) and stir-fry for a few seconds.

❹ Add the rice, egg and soy sauce to the pan. Mix gently, cover and cook gently until the rice is heated through.

Cook's note: You can use any type of rice you have available. Basmati rice will take 7–10 minutes to cook.

Fish or meat option: Make this into a main meal by adding 120 g (4 oz) of defrosted cooked, peeled prawns (add 1 extra Point and 55 Calories per serving) or 180 g (6 oz) of cooked chicken (add 1½ extra Points and 125 Calories per serving).

Variation: Add 120 g (4 oz) cooked peas (add 1 extra Point and 40 Calories per serving).

Mushroom Rice

This aromatic and creamy rice has a moist texture. No one would believe there's not a fresh mushroom or dollop of cream in sight! You've just got to try this recipe, which takes only 10 minutes of your time and yet tastes like a dish from a posh restaurant. It goes well with any type of cuisine.

Serves: 4
Preparation time: 10 minutes + 5 minutes soaking
(optional)
Cooking time: 15 minutes
Calories per serving: 265
Points per serving: 4½
Total Points per recipe: 18
Freezing: recommended

240 g (8 oz) basmati or long-grain rice
283 g can of creamed mushrooms
½ teaspoon salt

❶ Wash the rice and, if you have time, soak it in plenty of warm water for 5 minutes.
❷ Make the creamed mushrooms up to 500 ml (18 fl oz) with boiling water. Place this in a pan which has a tight-fitting lid and bring to the boil.
❸ Add the drained rice and the salt. Stir gently and bring back to the boil.
❹ Cover and simmer over the lowest heat for 15 minutes, until the rice is soft and moist. Stir once during cooking. Serve immediately.

Cook's notes: Don't worry about any lumps from the creamed mushrooms. These will disappear when the dish is cooked.

For extra flavour, crumble a vegetable stock cube in the cooking water.

Meat option: Add 120 g (4 oz) of leftover cooked chicken at step 3. This version has 6½ Points and 310 Calories per serving.

Variation: Add a 326 g can of sweetcorn at step 3 to make this into a main vegetarian meal (add 1½ extra Points and 75 Calories per serving).

Noodles with Bean Sprouts

This delicately flavoured accompaniment goes well with all Chinese and Thai dishes. I sometimes make this into a meal in itself, by adding vegetables and any leftover meat.

Serves: 4
Preparation and cooking time: 15 minutes
Calories per serving: 230
Points per serving: 3
Total Points per recipe: 12
Freezing: recommended

180 g (6 oz) thread egg noodles
2 teaspoons sesame or corn oil
1 teaspoon crushed ginger
6 spring onions, sliced diagonally
360 g (12 oz) bean sprouts
4 tablespoons light soy sauce
chilli sauce (optional)
salt and freshly ground black pepper
sesame seeds, to garnish

❶ Cook the noodles in lightly salted, boiling water, according to the instructions on the packet. Drain.
❷ Meanwhile, heat a wok or large, non-stick pan. Swirl in the oil. Add the ginger, spring onions and bean sprouts and stir-fry for 2–3 minutes.

❸ Gently mix in the drained noodles, soy sauce, seasoning and chilli sauce, if using. Serve hot, topped with sesame seeds.

Diced Spiced Salad

Serves: 4
Preparation time: 15 minutes
Calories per serving: 75
Points per serving: 1/2
Total Points per recipe: 2
Freezing: not recommended

3 carrots, cubed
1/2 cucumber, cubed
1 red or yellow pepper, cut in small squares
1 spring onion (optional)
torn or chopped fresh coriander
For the dressing:
3 tablespoons low-fat natural yogurt
1/2 teaspoon curry powder
2 teaspoons vinegar
2 teaspoons olive oil
salt and freshly ground black pepper

❶ Put all the dressing ingredients into a jar. Close the lid tightly and shake the jar until all the ingredients are mixed well together.
❷ Pour this dressing over the prepared salad vegetables and toss well. Serve chilled.

Cook's note: If preparing this in advance, stir again just before serving.

Diced Spiced Salad
Noodles with Bean Sprouts

Short-cut Hot and Sour Soup

This warming soup is a variation on a Thai recipe. The traditional dish contains fresh chicken stock, Thai ginger, lemon grass and fresh chillies. As a speedy alternative, I've used a stock cube, crushed ginger from a jar, leeks (which are similar to lemon grass) and chilli sauce. It's a perfect choice if you like soup which has a slightly tangy flavour and a bit of a kick!

Serves: 1
Preparation and cooking time: 10 minutes
Calories per serving: 150
Total Points per recipe: $3^1/_2$
Freezing: not recommended

1 chicken stock cube
a good pinch of dried basil
5 cm (2-inch) piece of fresh leek, sliced
1 teaspoon Thai fish sauce (optional) or
    soy sauce

$1/_4$ teaspoon crushed ginger
1 tablespoon soy sauce
2 teaspoons wine or cider vinegar
leaves of a few fresh coriander sprigs, torn
3–4 drops of sesame oil
1 egg, beaten
salt and pepper and chilli sauce, to taste
bread roll, to serve

❶ Make up the stock by crumbling the stock cube into 240 ml (8 fl oz) of boiling water in a pan. Season to taste with salt, pepper and chilli sauce.

❷ Add all the other ingredients, except the sesame oil and the egg. Bring to the boil and cook until the leeks are tender (about 5 minutes).

❸ Add the sesame oil. Pour in the egg over the back of a fork and move the fork around, so the egg doesn't all fall in one place.

❹ Place the lid on the pan and allow the egg to set for one minute. Stir and serve piping hot, with the bread roll.

Vegetarian option: Replace the chicken stock with vegetable stock and omit the fish sauce.

Variation: You may like to add some chopped watercress, celery and spring onion so that there are more 'bits'.

Cook's note: Thai fish sauce is a savoury, slightly fishy-tasting sauce available from oriental food shops and most supermarkets.

Thai Chicken Wings

A finger-lickin' starter which also makes a nice supper dish, served with salad.

Serves: 6
Preparation time: 5 minutes + marinating
Cooking time: 10–15 minutes
Calories per serving: 260
Points per serving: 1
Total Points per recipe: 6
Freezing: not recommended

12 chicken wings (1.15 kg/2³/₄ lb)
For the marinade:
1 teaspoon olive oil
¹/₂ teaspoon sesame oil (optional)
1 teaspoon dried basil
¹/₂–³/₄ teaspoon chilli powder
2 tablespoons light soy sauce
1 teaspoon crushed garlic
a pinch of salt

❶ Preheat the grill. Line the grill pan with foil.
❷ Mix the marinade ingredients together and coat the chicken wings. Marinate for 10 minutes.

❸ Cook under a hot grill for 10–15 minutes, until cooked but still moist. Turn and baste regularly. Serve immediately.

Raita

A refreshing, yogurt-based accompaniment that helps to cool down those hot Indian meals! I often serve this with salad and pitta bread when I want a light meal.

Serves: 2
Preparation time: 5 minutes
Calories per serving: 45
Points per serving: 1
Total Points per recipe: 2
Freezing: not recommended

150 ml carton of low-fat natural yogurt
5 cm (2-inch) piece of cucumber, cubed
¹/₄ teaspoon dried mint
¹/₂ teaspoon ground cumin (optional)
a few fresh coriander sprigs, chopped
salt and freshly ground black pepper

❶ Mix all the ingredients together and serve chilled.

Cook's note: If you are preparing this in advance, add the cucumber just before serving.

Variations: Add chopped spring onions or green pepper, if you like a bit more crunch.

Make this into a more substantial snack by adding 120 g (4 oz) chopped boiled potato (add 1 extra Point and 45 Calories per serving) or 105 g (3¹/₂ oz) of drained, canned chick-peas (add 1 extra Point and 50 Calories per serving).

Raita
Thai Chicken Wings

Instant Chilli and Lemon Chutney

A tangy accompaniment to a mild Indian meal for those who like a bit of extra zing! This chutney goes well with Lamb Tikka (page 20) and Thai Chicken Wings (page 40). It is extra special as it has almost no Points!

Serves: 4
Preparation time: 5 minutes
Calories per serving: 15
Total Points per recipe: 1/2
Freezing: not recommended

3 tablespoons tomato ketchup
1–2 tablespoons lemon juice
1–2 teaspoons chilli powder
1/2 teaspoon garlic grain pepper or coarse ground black pepper
1 teaspoon Worcestershire sauce
1 tablespoon finely chopped fresh coriander (optional)

1 Simply mix all the ingredients together and taste to see if the balance of hotness, sharpness and sweetness is to your liking. Adjust and serve.

Variation: Add a finely chopped tomato. This will add an extra 20 Calories per serving. The Points will remain the same.

Coriander and Coconut Chutney

This thick Thai/Indian chutney is almost like a salad. It's not a dipping sauce but is something you'd have at the side of the plate to mix in a little at a time with your meal. If you have a liquidiser, you may like to purée it. I like to serve this with rice dishes or use it to spice up Western foods.

Serves: 4
Preparation time: 10 minutes
Calories per serving: 15
Points per serving: 1
Total Points per recipe: 4
Freezing: not recommended

15 g packet of fresh coriander leaves, chopped finely
2 tablespoons lemon juice
1/4 teaspoon chilli powder, or to taste
2 tablespoons desiccated coconut
salt

1 Mix everything together with 7 tablespoons of water and it's ready!

Desserts

When you fancy something sweet to round off the meal, it doesn't always have to be fruit. These unusual desserts provide the ideal finishing touch to your Eastern meal and take less than 20 minutes to prepare. Indian and Chinese desserts are often high in Points, since they may contain a lot of butter, oil, sugar or cream. The difference here is that you'll be using lower-fat ingredients with no added sugar, so you get all the taste without the dismal effect on your waistline!

Mango and Kiwi Pudding

Serves: 2
Preparation and cooking time: 20 minutes
Calories per serving: 180
Points per serving: 3
Total Points per recipe: 6
Freezing: not recommended

1 large mango, peeled, stoned and cut in small pieces
1 passion-fruit (optional)
150 g (5 oz) very-low-fat fromage frais
2 tablespoons granulated artificial sweetener
1/2 bar chocolate flake, crumbled
1 kiwi fruit, peeled and sliced

❶ Mix the mango and the pulp and seeds of the passion-fruit, if using, together.
❷ Beat the fromage frais with the sweetener. Mix this creamy mixture with the mango and place in two glass serving dishes.
❸ Sprinkle the crumbled chocolate on to this and decorate with sliced kiwi fruit. Serve chilled.

Cook's note: The best way to prepare mangoes is to peel them and then cut down either side of the large central stone. You can then cut the flesh as required.

Don't forget to make use of the flesh surrounding the stone!

Weight Watchers note: Artificial sweeteners are virtually Calorie-free and have 0 Points.

Variation: If you don't like the taste of fromage frais, use 105 ml (3 1/2 fl oz) low-fat whipping cream and add 2 Points and 105 Calories per serving.

Mango and Kiwi Pudding
Stuffed Lychees

Stuffed Lychees

This pudding is perfect for taming your tastebuds after a spicy meal.

Serves: 3
Preparation time: 15 minutes
Calories per serving: 155
Points per serving: 3
Total Points per recipe: 9
Freezing: not recommended

75 g (2¹/₂ oz) medium-fat soft cheese
3 teaspoons desiccated coconut
1 teaspoon honey
a pinch of ground ginger (optional)
2 teaspoons ground almonds
425 g can of lychees, drained

❶ Mix the cheese with 2 teaspoons of the coconut and all the other ingredients, except the lychees.
❷ Preheat the grill. Using the handle of a teaspoon, stuff the hole of each lychee with the cheese mixture.
❸ Toast the remaining teaspoon of coconut under the grill for a few seconds.

❹ Place the stuffed lychees in a serving dish and sprinkle with toasted coconut. Serve chilled.

Sizzling Bananas

A sweet-smelling and piping-hot dessert which the Govindji family could eat any day of the week! It's an excellent way to round off a Chinese meal, especially one that leaves you just a little bit hungry. The orange shreds contrast beautifully with the white nuts or seeds.

Serves: 4
Preparation and cooking time: 15 minutes
Calories per serving: 165
Points per serving: 2¹/₂
Total Points per recipe: 10
Freezing: not recommended

30 g (1 oz) reduced-fat mono-unsaturated spread
zest and juice of 1 large orange
4 bananas, peeled and cut diagonally in four
1 tablespoon chopped nuts or sesame seeds

❶ Melt the spread in a non-stick pan. Add the orange zest and banana pieces. Cook gently until the bananas are soft (about 5 minutes).

❷ Add the orange juice. Sprinkle with nuts or sesame seeds and serve immediately.

Index